# Look at Me
## I'm going to
## Germany!

AIRPORT

D1530413

This book is dedicated
to my daughter
Carmela

First published in 2021 by Daniel Williamson
www.danielwilliamson.co.uk
This edition published in 2021
Text © Daniel Williamson 2021
Illustrations © Kleverton Monteiro 2021
Cover design © by Uzuri Designs 2021

Translated by Jessica Kallweit

All rights reserved. No part of this publication may be reproduced, stored in a retrieval system
or transmitted, in any form or by any means, electronic, mechanical, photocopying,
recording or otherwise, without the prior permission of the copyright holder.

ISBN 978-1-913583-27-9

DW

www.danielwilliamson.co.uk

I woke up so excited today, because today I'm going to Germany for the first time ever! I just can't wait!

Ich bin heute sehr aufgeregt aufgewacht, weil ich heute zum allerersten Mal nach Deutschland gehe! Ich kann es nicht erwarten!

At the airport I got to have my photo taken with the pilot before our flight to Berlin.

Am Flughafen ließ ich mich vor unseren Flug nach Berlin mit dem Piloten fotografieren.

When we arrived in Berlin I met my German family. They were very happy to see me. They brought their puppy to meet me, his name is Bello.

Als wir in Berlin ankamen, habe ich meine deutsche Familie getroffen. Sie waren sehr glücklich mich zu sehen. Sie haben ihren Welpen mitgebracht, um mich zu treffen. Sein Name ist Bello.

We went to the family home and had a traditional German meal. We ate Sauerbraten, potato dumplings, and red cabbage. I love German food!

Wir sind zum Haus der Familie gefahren und hatten ein traditionelles deutsches Essen. Wir haben Sauerbraten, Kartoffelknödel und Rotkohl gegessen.
Ich liebe deutsches Essen!

After dinner my uncle played a famous German song on his piano. The song was called 'All Birds Are Already There.' German music is beautiful!

Nach dem Abendessen hat mein Onkel ein berühmtes deutsches Lied auf dem Klavier gespielt. Das Lied hieß: „Alle Vögel sind schon da." Deutsche Musik ist schön!

At bedtime my grandmother read me a story called 'Rübezahl' about a friendly giant in the German mountains called 'The Giant Mountains.'

Zur Schlafenszeit hat mir meine Großmutter eine Geschichte namens Rübezahl vorgelesen, über einen freundlichen Riesen in den deutschen Bergen die „Riesengebirge" heißen.

The next day we went to see the Brandenbourg Gate. It was built in the 1730s by Frederick William II of Prussia to represent peace and was originally named the Peace Gate.

Am nächsten Tag haben wir das Brandenburger Tor besichtigt. Es wurde in den 1730er Jahren von Friedrich Wilhelm II von Preußen gebaut, um Frieden zu symbolisieren und hieß ursprünglich Friedenstor.

Then we went to a museum called 'Gemäldegalerie.'
I saw multiple, beautiful, German paintings and statues.
Some were over 800 years old!

Dann sind wir zu einem Museum gegangen, dass
„Gemäldegalerie" hieß. Ich habe viele schöne
deutsche Gemälde und Statuen gesehen. Einige
waren mehr als 800 Jahre alt!

My favourite paintings were by a man called Albrecht Dürer. I wish I could paint like that!

Meine Lieblingsbilder waren von einem Mann namens Albrecht Dürer. Ich wünschte ich könnte so malen!

Outside the museum was a man selling pretzels.
It's a very tasty German snack.
I ate two of them all by myself!

Vor dem Museum war ein Mann, der Brezeln verkauft
hat. Das ist ein sehr leckerer deutscher Snack.
Ich habe zwei davon ganz alleine gegessen.

We walked to Alexanderplatz and I saw two people doing a traditional German dance. It was called 'schuhplattler.' It was wonderful to watch.

Wir sind zum Alexanderplatz gegangen und ich habe gesehen wie zwei Leute einen traditionellen, deutschen Tanz getanzt haben.
Er hieß „Schuhplattler ". Es war toll zuzusehen.

In the afternoon we went to the Olympic Stadium to watch Germany play football. A nice lady gave me a German flag to wave!

Am Nachmittag sind wir zum Olympiastadion gefahren, um Deutschland spielen zu sehen. Eine nette Dame hat mir eine deutsche Fahne zum Schwenken gegeben!

The football was really fun! Dad bought me a T-Shirt like the players. I was shouting "Go on Germany! One more goal!"

Das Fußballspiel hat viel Spaß gemacht! Papa hat mir ein Trikot wie die Spieler gekauft. Ich habe "Deutschland vor, noch ein Tor!" gerufen.

After the match we went to a restaurant for more yummy German food. I had Currywurst and Black Forest Gateau for dessert!

Nach dem Spiel sind wir in ein Restaurant gegangen, um noch mehr leckeres deutsches Essen zu essen. Ich hatte Curry Wurst und Schwarzwälder Kirschtorte zum Nachtisch!

The waiter was really funny. He even did a magic trick just for me. His name was Hans and he is from Cologne.

Der Kellner war wirklich lustig. Er hat sogar nur für mich einen Zaubertrick gemacht. Sein Name war Hans und er kam aus Köln.

In the morning it was really sunny and we all
went to an orchard. Apples grow a lot here.
I picked some from the trees.
Am Morgen war es wirklich sonnig und wir sind alle zu
einem Obstgarten gegangen. Es wachsen viele Äpfel
hier. Ich habe welche von den Bäumen gepflückt.

I met a nice old lady there and she was wearing a 'dirndl.' It's a traditional dress from Bavaria.

Ich habe dort eine nette alte Dame getroffen und sie hat ein "Dirndl" getragen. Das ist ein traditionelles Kleid in Bayern.

In the car I heard different German music called 'Schlager.' I liked this German music too, it made me want to dance!

In dem Auto habe ich andere deutsche Musik gehört, die Schlager heißt. Ich mochte diese Musik auch. Sie machte Lust zu tanzen!

We drove past an old building called the Bundestag. It's famous because the politicians work there. Over 700 of them represent the German people.

Wir sind an einem alten Gebäude vorbeigefahren, das "Bundestag" heißt. Es ist berühmt, weil dort die Politiker arbeiten. Mehr als 700 von ihnen repräsentieren die deutschen Leute.

Back at the house, on our last night, my German family and I all played a game together called 'Settlers of Catan.' It was really fun!

Zurück im Haus, während unserer letzten Nacht, haben meine deutsche Familie und ich ein Spiel zusammen gespielt, das "Siedler von Catan" heißt. Es hat viel Spaß gemacht!

Before I went to bed my German family gave me
a present each to remind me of Germany.
They gave me a Berliner bear, a cuckoo clock
and a Milka chocolate bar.

Bevor ich ins Bett gegangen bin, hat mir meine deutsche
Familie jeweils ein Geschenk gegeben, um mich an
Deutschland zu erinnern. Sie gaben mir einen Berliner
Bären, eine Kuckucksuhr und eine Milka Schokoladentafel.

I really love it in Germany! The only problem is I can't decide what's my favourite thing

Ich liebe es wirklich in Deutschland! Das einzige Problem ist, dass ich nicht entscheiden kann was am besten ist.

Was it the yummy German food,
the German music, the lovely German gifts,
the 'Schuhplattler' dancing...

War es das leckere deutsche Essen,
die deutsche Musik, die wundervollen deutschen
Geschenke, der „Schuhplattlertanz"...

Or was it the art by Albrecht Durer,
the beautiful German monuments, the 'Rubezahl'
story or spending time with my German family...

Oder war es die Kunst von Albrecht Dürer, die schönen
deutschen Monumente, die „Rübezahlgeschichte" oder
Zeit mit meiner deutschen Familie zu verbringen...

I just can't decide because I love everything here!
So much so, in fact...

Ich kann mich einfach nicht entscheiden, weil
ich alles hier liebe! Tatsächlich so sehr...

... that I've already asked to come back real soon. Again and again and again.

... dass ich schon gefragt habe, ob ich sehr bald zurückkommen kann. Wieder und wieder und wieder.

This author has developed a bilingual book series designed to introduce children to a number of new languages from a very young age.

If you enjoyed reading this story, you will undoubtedly like popular rhyming picture books from this author which are also currently available.

# A Message From The Author

I'd like to say a massive thank you to every single child and adult that read one of my books! My dream is to bring cultures together through fun illustrations, imagination and creativity via the power of books.

If you would like to join me on this journey, please visit my website danielwilliamson.co.uk where each email subscriber receives a free ebook to keep or we will happily send to a friend of your choice as a gift!

Nothing makes me happier than a review on the platform you purchased my book telling me where my readers are from! Also, please click on my links below and follow me to join my ever-growing online family! Remember there is no time like the present and the present is a gift!

Yours gratefully

## Daniel Williamson

@DanWAuthor

@danwauthor

@DanWAuthor

Made in the USA
Monee, IL
07 November 2022

17141973R00021